JOHANN SEBASTIAN BACH

(1685-1750)

LITTLE FUGUES AND LITTLE PRELUDES AND FUGUES

Edited by Keith Snell

CONTENTS

ISBN 0-8497-6270-7

©1999 Neil A. Kjos Music Company, 4380 Jutland Drive, San Diego, California 92117

THE BAROQUE PERIOD

The word *baroque* was originally used to describe a style of art and architecture of highly decorative and extravagant design in the 17th and 18th centuries. It is not until the 20th century that the term is used to describe the style of music from approximately 1600 to 1750. J. S. Bach is regarded as the greatest composer of the Baroque period.

JOHANN SEBASTIAN BACH (1685-1750)

Johann Sebastian Bach was born in Eisenach—a small town in central Germany. He came from a very musical family. For almost 200 years before his birth, many of his relatives were well known musicians in Germany. Bach received his first music lessons from his father who taught him to play the violin.

Bach was only 10 years old when his parents died. He then went to live with his older brother, Johann Christoph, who taught him to play keyboard instruments. In addition to his music lessons, he attended the local school where he studied Latin, Greek, theology, and arithmetic.

In 1700 when Bach was 15 years old, he went to live at the church of St. Michael in Lüneburg where he was a choir boy and student. After his voice changed, he continued serving in various musical jobs which began his career as a professional musician.

At the age of 19, he took a job in Weimar as string player and organist. A few months later he found a better position as organist in Arnstadt. He moved again to Mühlhausen where he stayed one year. During this year Bach married his cousin, Maria Barbara Bach. During their marriage they had seven children, but only four lived.

After the year at Mühlhausen, Bach returned to Weimar where he spent nine years employed as composer and organist at the court of Duke Wilhelm Ernst. Disappointed at not being promoted to Music Director, Bach moved on to the court of Prince Leopold of Anhalt in the city of Cöthen. Here Bach became Music Director, in charge of the Prince's singers and the court orchestra.

In 1720 Maria Barbara died. One year later he married his second wife, Anna Magdalena, who was only 20 years old. They had 13 children. Out of the 20 children from Bach's two marriages, 10 died in infancy or at childbirth. From the surviving 10, four of his sons—Carl Philipp Emanuel, Johann Christoph, Johann Christian and Wilhelm Friedemann—became composers.

When he was 38, Bach moved to Leipzig where he became cantor (music teacher) at the St. Thomas School. He remained there until his death 27 years later. During these years Bach was very busy teaching, conducting, performing, and writing music.

In 1750, the last year of his life, Bach's eyesight began to deteriorate. By summer, his health failed and he died on July 28. He was buried in St. John's cemetery. Anna Magdalena lived ten more years, but died in poverty in 1760.

Bach was a prolific composer. His complete works fill 46 large volumes containing choral music, concertos, orchestra and chamber works, and organ and clavier (keyboard) music.

PRELUDE

A **prelude** is a composition intended to precede a larger work or group of pieces. Preludes evolved from improvisations by musicians testing the tuning, touch or tone of their instrument. In the Baroque period, a prelude followed by a fugue or suite of dances became the most common type.

FUGUE

Fugue is the most highly evolved style of imitative polyphonic music from the Baroque period. It was brought to perfection by J.S. Bach.

Although the fugue does not have an exact form, there are basic principals and characteristics in the structure of a fugue. The overall structure of a fugue is the imitation of a subject and a countersubject (or derived motives) in alternating sections called expositions and episodes.

- **Polyphonic Texture**: Fugues are always written in polyphonic texture. A fugue may have two or more voices, however, fugues with three or four voices are the most common.

- **Subject**: Fugues are based on a short melody called the subject. The subject is stated at the beginning of the fugue in one voice and is immediately imitated by the other voices. The subject will be stated many times throughout the fugue in all the voices.

- **Answer**: The imitation of the subject in another key, usually the dominant, is called the answer. Answers may be real or tonal. A real answer is an exact transposition of the subject. A tonal answer has modified intervals.

- **Countersubject**: The countersubject is a contrasting melody that is stated in the first voice immediately after the subject as the second voice imitates the subject. The countersubject may be derived from motives in the subject or may be a continuation of the subject. The countersubject will be stated many times throughout the fugue in all the voices.

- **Exposition**: A section in which the subject is stated at least once in each voice is called an exposition. A fugue may have three, four or more expositions. The term exposition is sometimes used only for the first exposition, without any special name for the later sections of similar construction. Later expositions usually involve modulations to other keys such as the relative minor, dominant, or subdominant, with a return to the tonic key in the last exposition.

- **Episode**: A section of the fugue which does not include a statement of the subject is called an episode. The exposition sections are separated from one another by episodes. Episodes are usually based on motives from the subject or countersubject. These motives are frequently used in sequences. The episodes, although still in strict polyphonic style, are somewhat freer in structure than expositions.

Fugue in C Minor

BWV 961

FUGUE IN C MAJOR

BWV 952

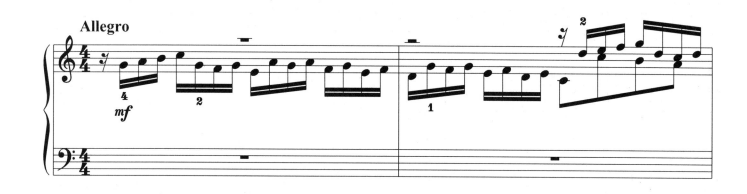

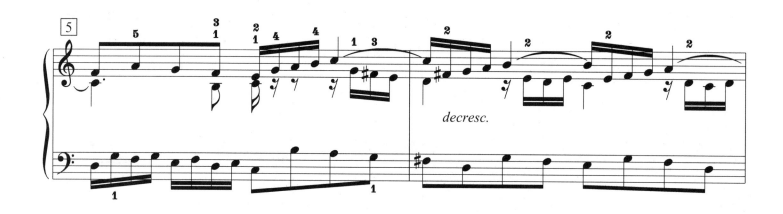

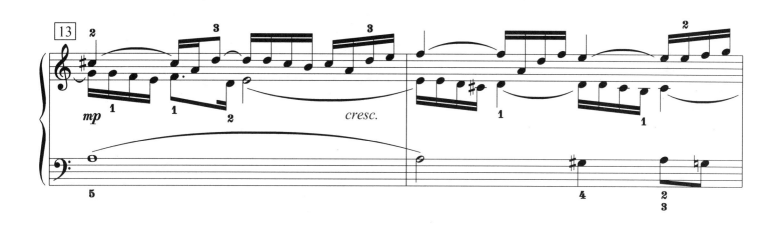

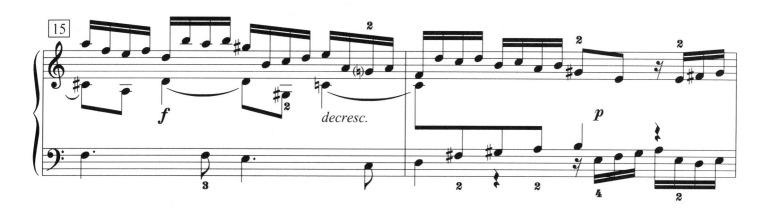

FUGUE IN C MAJOR

BWV 953

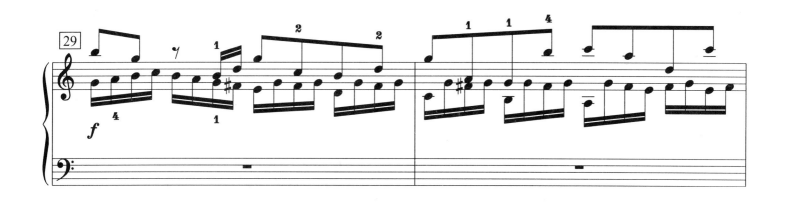

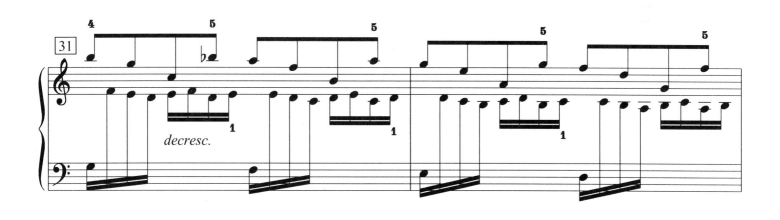

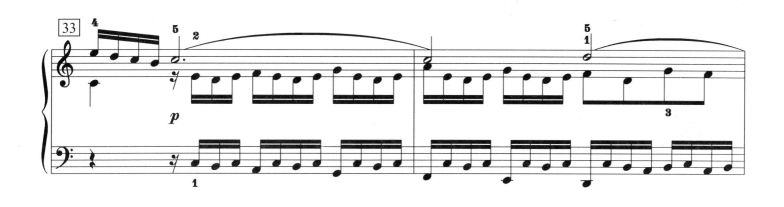

PRELUDE AND FUGUE IN G MAJOR

BWV 902

Prelude
Allegro

© 1999 Neil A. Kjos Music Company, 4380 Jutland Drive, San Diego, California, 92117.

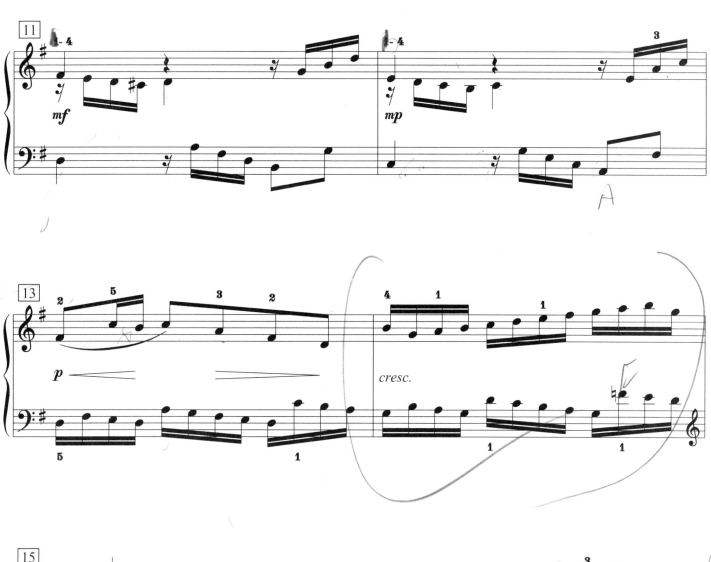

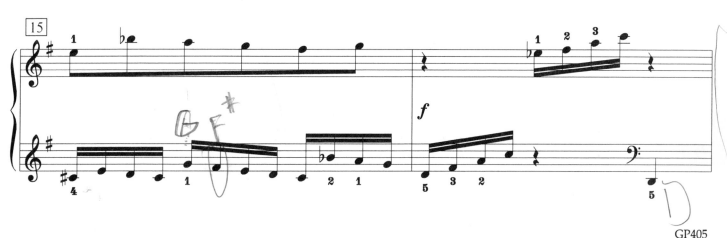

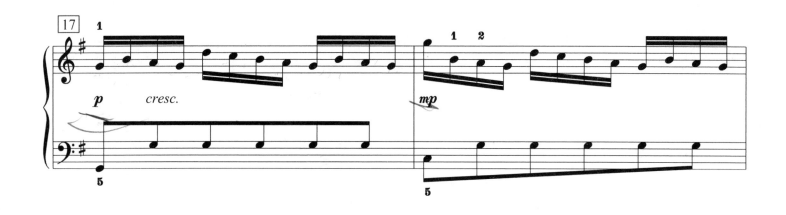

Fugue

Allegretto

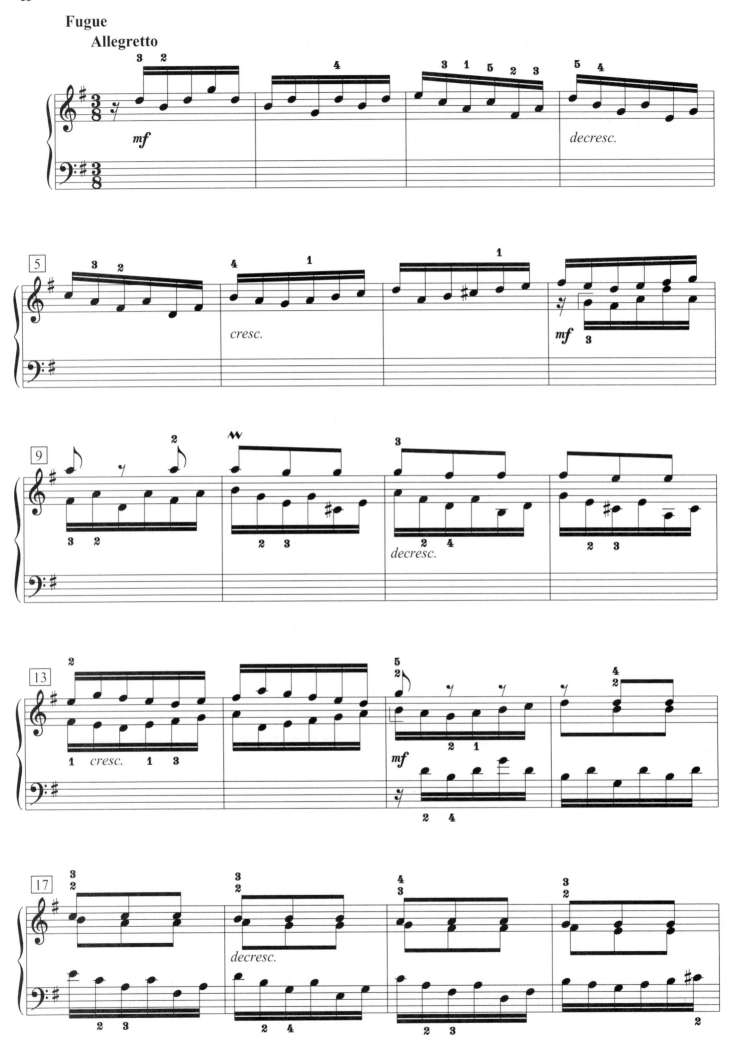

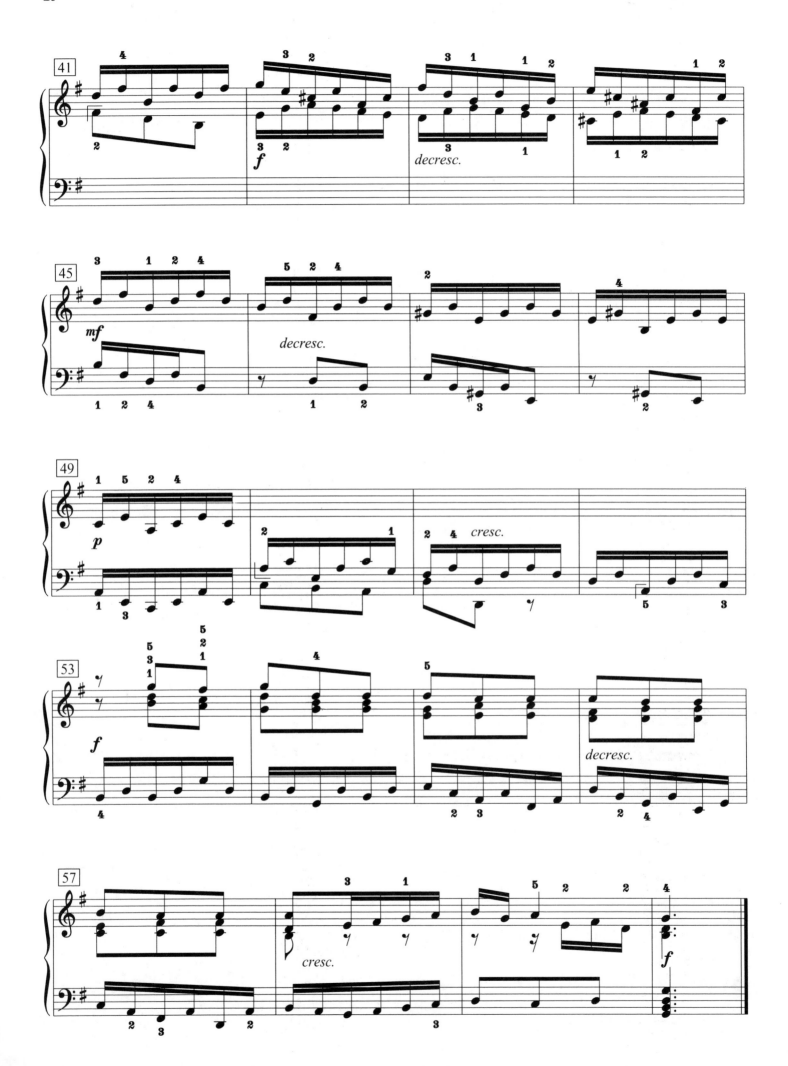

PRELUDE AND FUGUE IN A MINOR

BWV 895

© 1999 Neil A. Kjos Music Company, 4380 Jutland Drive, San Diego, California, 92117.

Fugue

Allegro

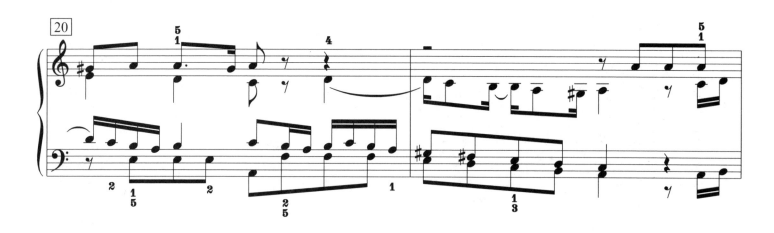

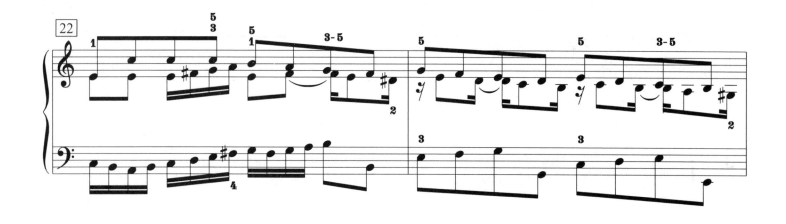

PRELUDE AND FUGUE IN E MINOR

Prelude

BWV 900

Andante

© 1999 Neil A. Kjos Music Company, 4380 Jutland Drive, San Diego, California, 92117.

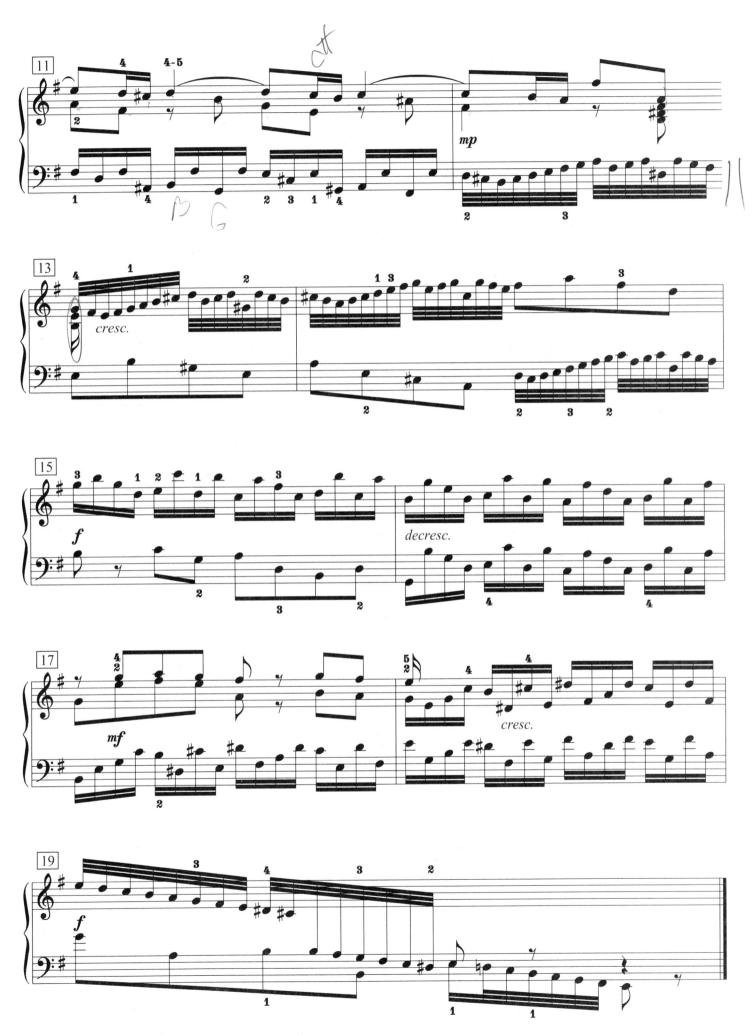

Fugue

Allegretto

30

GP405

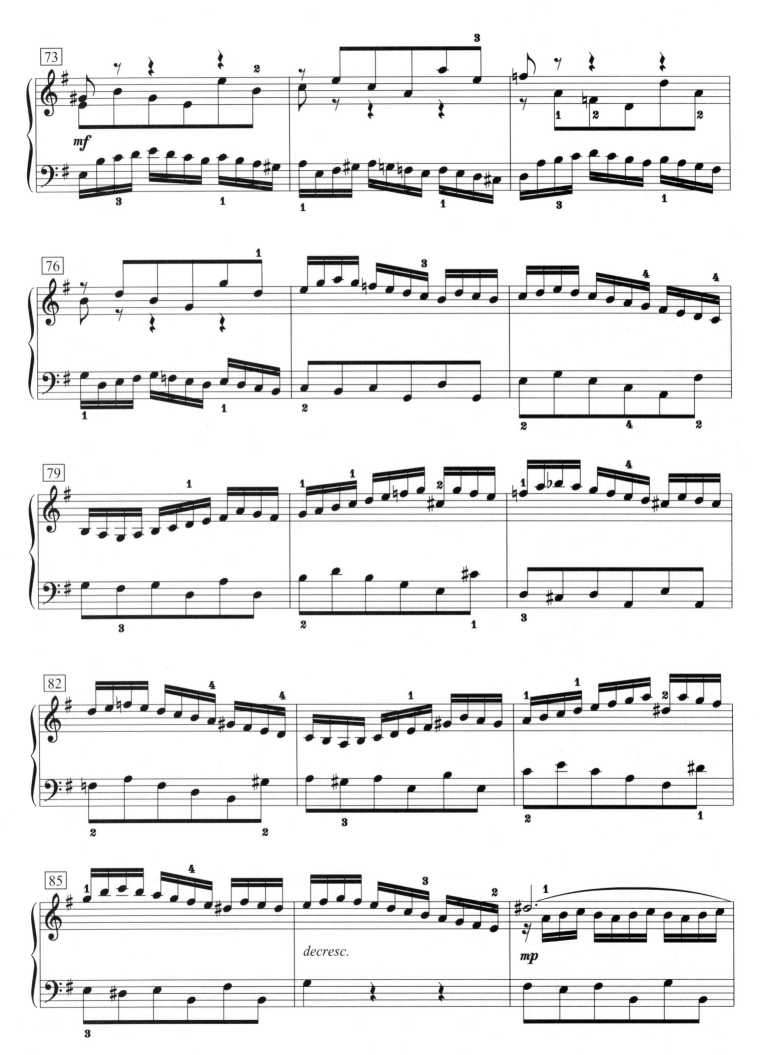

PRELUDE AND FUGUE IN D MINOR

BWV 899

Prelude

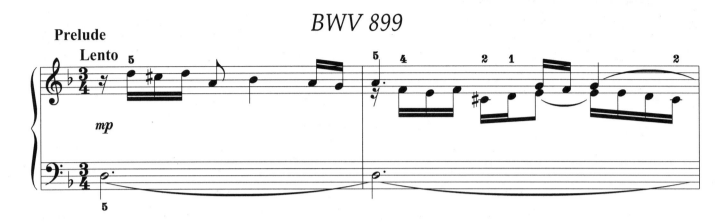

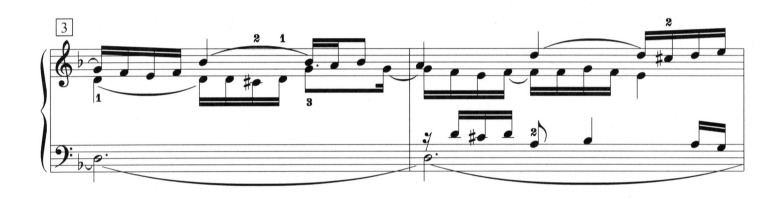

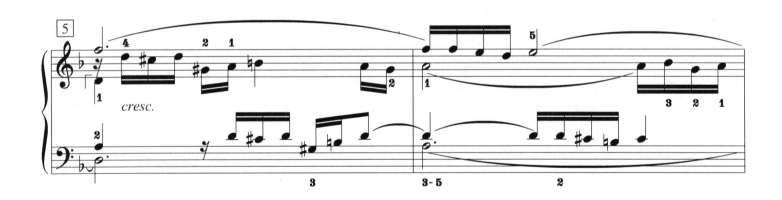

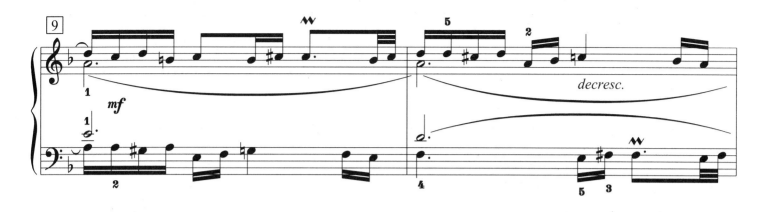

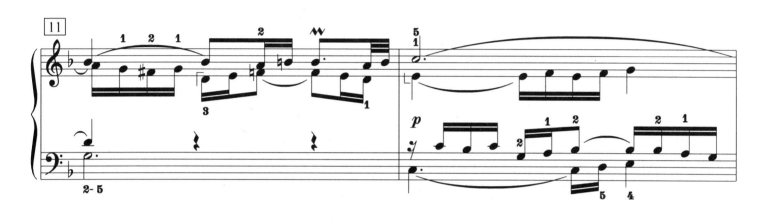

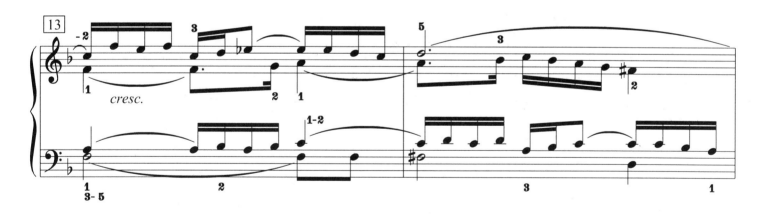

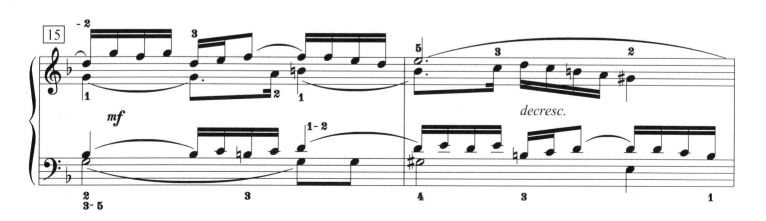

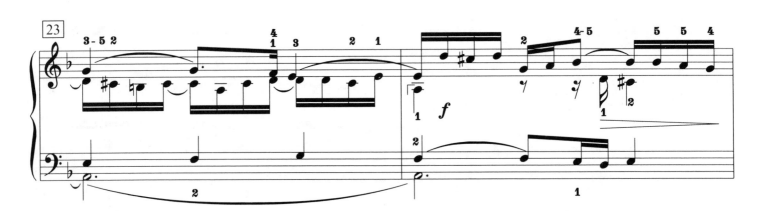

Fugue
Allegretto

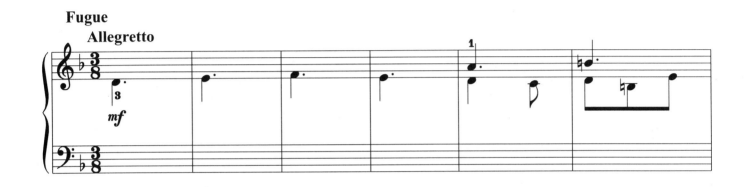

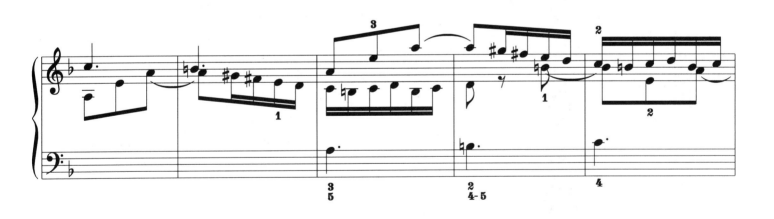

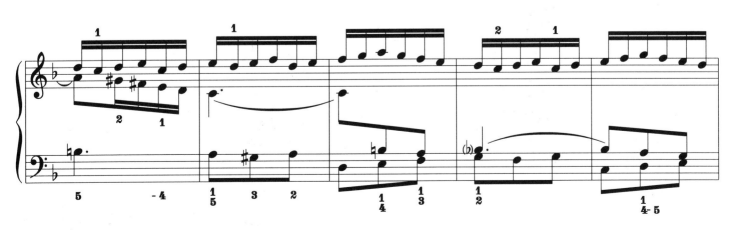

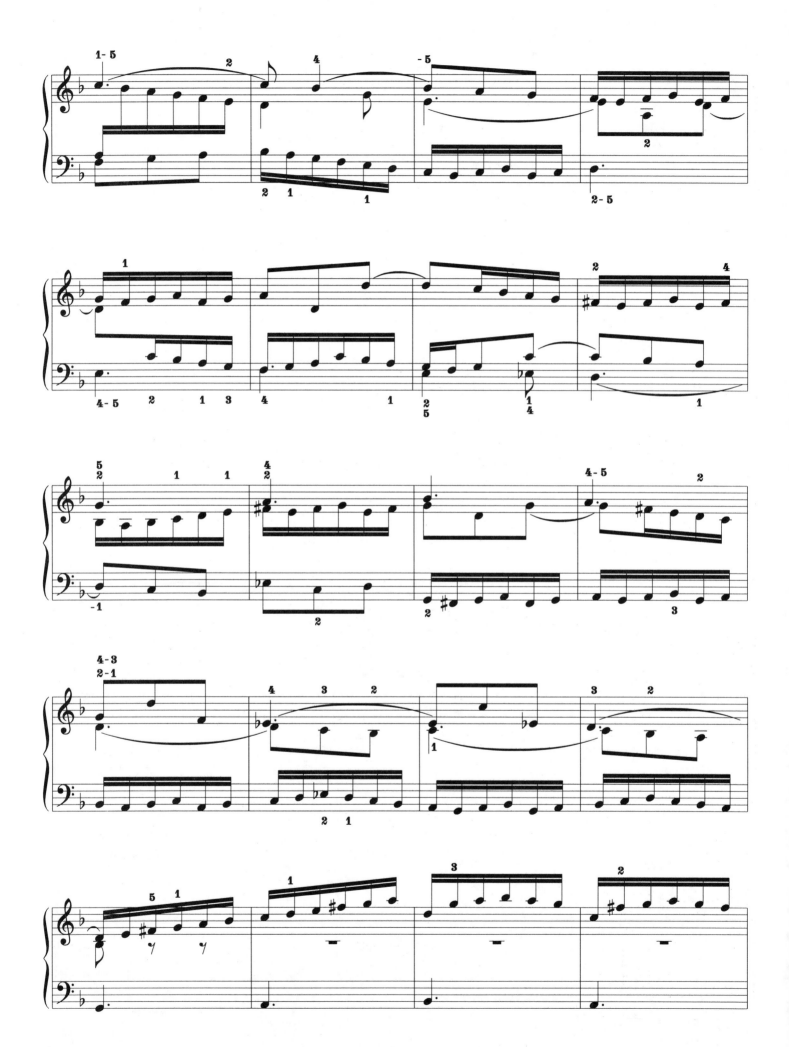

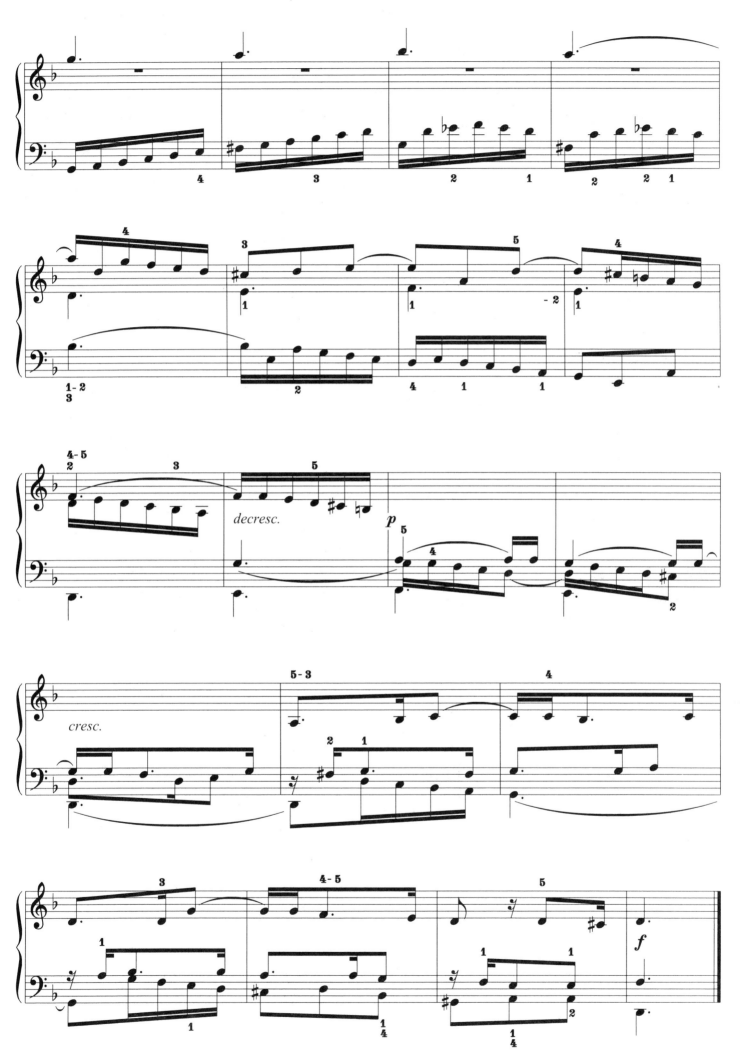

TABLE OF ORNAMENTS

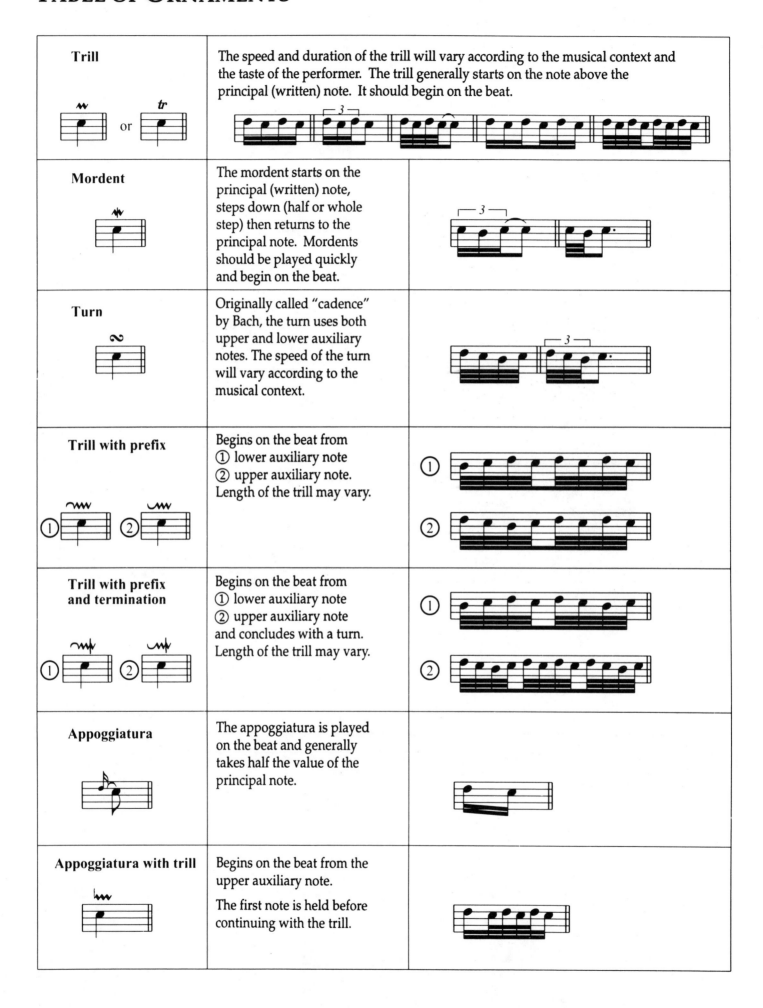

Trill	The speed and duration of the trill will vary according to the musical context and the taste of the performer. The trill generally starts on the note above the principal (written) note. It should begin on the beat.	
Mordent	The mordent starts on the principal (written) note, steps down (half or whole step) then returns to the principal note. Mordents should be played quickly and begin on the beat.	
Turn	Originally called "cadence" by Bach, the turn uses both upper and lower auxiliary notes. The speed of the turn will vary according to the musical context.	
Trill with prefix	Begins on the beat from ① lower auxiliary note ② upper auxiliary note. Length of the trill may vary.	
Trill with prefix and termination	Begins on the beat from ① lower auxiliary note ② upper auxiliary note and concludes with a turn. Length of the trill may vary.	
Appoggiatura	The appoggiatura is played on the beat and generally takes half the value of the principal note.	
Appoggiatura with trill	Begins on the beat from the upper auxiliary note. The first note is held before continuing with the trill.	